100 YEARS OF POPULAR

40s - Volume 1

Series Editor:
Carol Cuellar

Editorial and Production:
Artemis Music Limited

Design and Production:
JPCreativeGroup.com

Published 2003

International Music Publications Limited
Griffin House 161 Hammersmith Road London W6 8BS England

International
MUSIC
Publications

CONTENTS

40s

Hitler will send no warning – so always carry your gas mask

ISSUED BY THE MINISTRY OF HOME SECURITY

Ordinary people rose to meet extraordinary challenges in the 1940s. The sons and daughters of the Great Depression, who struggled for even the most basic of life's necessities in the '30s, grew into the men and women who, in this new decade, would battle and win a terrible war against history's most wicked and dangerous tyrant.

For much of 1940 and 1941, the UK stood alone against Hitler's war machine. The Battle Of France was over; the Battle Of Britain had begun. With it came daily bombing raids, sometimes by as many as 1500 German aircraft, on London, Coventry, Liverpool, and other cities. For the people who lived and worked in these cities, the horrors of war suddenly became as intimate and personal as the bombed-out building across the street, or the loved one lost in a night-time raid.

Yet, nothing could break the will of this generation. People not only fought the battle, they defied their tormentors by going about their daily lives with a measure of confidence and spirited determination. In so doing, they sent an unmistakable message to Hitler and his henchmen – you will not frighten us! The remarkable men and women of the '40s drew

strength from the music of this era. Music not only lifted their spirits, it restored a sense of normality to their lives. The bombers still visited their nightly terror on the cities, familiar landmarks were reduced to rubble, ration cards and dry, tasteless "national loaf" bread became dreary facts of everyday life, but one could still be swept away by the romantic refrains of the Hoagy Carmichael-penned tune "The Nearness Of You" or "I Don't Want To Set The World On Fire" by The Ink Spots.

Songs of Separation

Music also warmed the heart and soul by evoking tender memories of other times and places. The London-born singer Vera Lynn brought this comforting message to her generation with hit songs like "White Cliffs Of Dover" and "Yours". Born only a year before the previous war ended, the beautiful young songbird was blessed with a warmth and innocence that was sorely needed during the bleak days of the early '40s.

Lynn was named the host of the BBC radio program "Sincerely Yours" in 1940 and quickly became a star among the soldiers and sailors who tuned into the programme overseas. Known as "The Forces Sweetheart", Lynn's endearing personality and soft, lovely voice reminded everyone of the pretty girl back home. Her fame continued to spread after the war, and in 1952 she had the distinction of being the first British artist to reach the No. 1 position on the US charts – years before there even was a group called The Beatles!

As the war progressed, and the tide of the battle changed in favour of the Allies, the separation songs that were popular in Britain and America became more optimistic. Now, instead of merely longing for a faraway love, crooners were more apt to sing about the lovers' reunion that would take place when the war ended.

This sentiment is evident in the 1944 hit "I'll Be Seeing You". The team of

Irving Kahal and Sammy

Fain wrote this song for the Broadway show *Right This Way*, a production that failed to attract much interest when it debuted in 1938. Yet, both Bing Crosby and Tommy Dorsey enjoyed smash hits with the song six years later, when a growing sense of optimism about the war gave new meaning to the lines, "I'll be seeing you, in all the old familiar places".

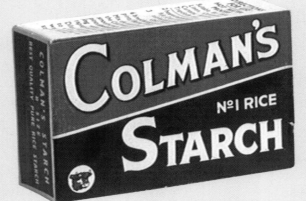

long after their time had drawn to a close. Their words and deeds still inspire awe today, and leave us with a sense that we may never see their likes again.

The world of music was also populated by giants in the '40s. From singers like Frank Sinatra ("Almost Like Being In Love"), to band leaders like Harry James ("You'll Never Know") and jazz innovators like bebop saxophonist Charlie Parker ("Laura"), the '40s witnessed the emergence of superstars whose innovative ideas would influence the course of popular music for generations to come.

A Time Of Giants

Although the '40s were a decade of uncommon courage by common people, they were also a time of giants. Churchill, Roosevelt, Montgomery, De Gaulle, Patton ... the figures that strode across the world stage in those ten eventful years would leave large and indelible footprints. Their images and voices would remain instantly recognisable to millions born

Among the most influential musical stars of the '40s were Ella Fitzgerald and Duke Ellington. A teenage prodigy who burst upon the music scene in the middle of the '30s as a member of Chick Webb's band, Fitzgerald emerged as an international star in the '40s with hits like "How High The Moon."

Fitzgerald won over audiences everywhere through her sweet voice, facile rhythm, and the sheer joy she

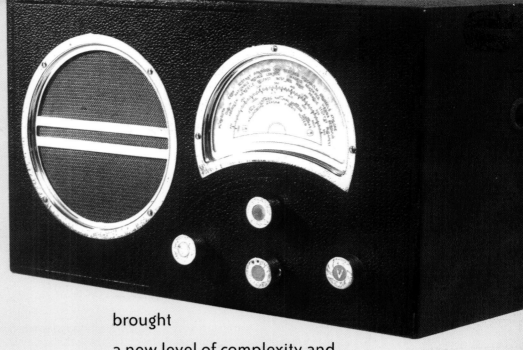

brought to her music. Holding nothing back, she didn't merely sing songs as much as celebrate them, improvising lyrics with animated spontaneity. Her magical voice, with its gleeful bounce, soared like a bird in flight, bringing the art of jazz singing to new heights and setting a standard for performers of future generations.

Among Fitzgerald's most memorable performances are those she gave with the Duke Ellington Orchestra. A composer, pianist, and band leader of incomparable genius, Ellington infused the popular swing dance music of the era with a stylish and sophisticated jazz influence. In so doing, he

brought a new level of complexity and emotional depth to big band music, while keeping it perfectly accessible to a broad audience.

Ellington's genius for blending different musical influences into his own distinctive jazz motif is on full display in the hit "Don't Get Around Much Any More". Interestingly, Ellington originally wrote this song as an instrumental, "Never No Lament," in 1940. Lyricist Bob Russell was so taken with the song that he added words to it to create "Don't Get Around Much Anymore," which promptly became a major hit in Great Britain and America.

Throughout his long and distinguished career, Ellington enjoyed a large and loyal following in Great Britain. During one of the great band leader's earlier visits to England, he encountered another "Duke." A great fan of Ellington's music, the Duke of Windsor once sat in with the famous band and played the drums.

WOMEN OF BRITAIN
COME INTO THE FACTORIES
ASK AT ANY EMPLOYMENT EXCHANGE FOR ADVICE AND FULL DETAILS

Like Ellington, Londoner Edward "Ted" Heath was an exquisitely talented musician (trombone), composer, and orchestra leader, who successfully blended a variety of musical influences into his big band sound. "That Lovely Weekend", a song that Heath wrote with his wife, Moira Tracey, was a major hit in the '40s.

Heath hired out the London Palladium to hold his "Sunday Night Swing Session". Although some critics suggested that the Palladium was too large for such an event, the sessions proved hugely successful and were carried on for years, serving as a showcase for new jazz and swing talent.

As for Heath, he continued to enjoy success, recording albums and performing at concerts well into the 1960s. The Ted Heath Big Band along with many other British bands of the '40s, was still attracting new fans long after the war years had passed. Like the momentous events that shaped the '40s, the great bands and music of this decade will never be forgotten.

A BRAND NEW CAR FOR A BRIGHT NEW WORLD

THE NEW **1947** *Studebaker*

Ten Things That First Appeared In The '40s

1. **The aerosol spray can.**

2. **Velcro (George de Mestral of Switzerland).**

3. **Nuclear reactor (Enrico Fermi of Italy).**

4. **Kidney dialysis machine (Willem J. Kolff, Dutch medical researcher).**

5. **Mobile phones.**

6. **Cake mix.**

7. **Guided missile.**

8. **Tesco self-service stores.**

9. **Microwave oven.**

10. **LP records.**

ALL OF A SUDDEN MY HEART SINGS

Words by HAROLD ROME
Music by JAMBLAN and HENRI LAURENT HERPIN

Slow rock

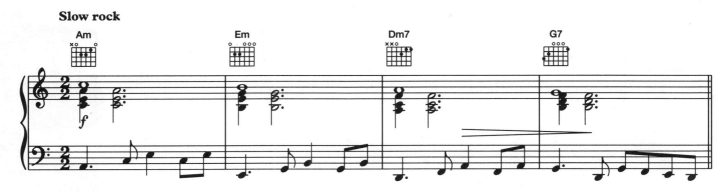

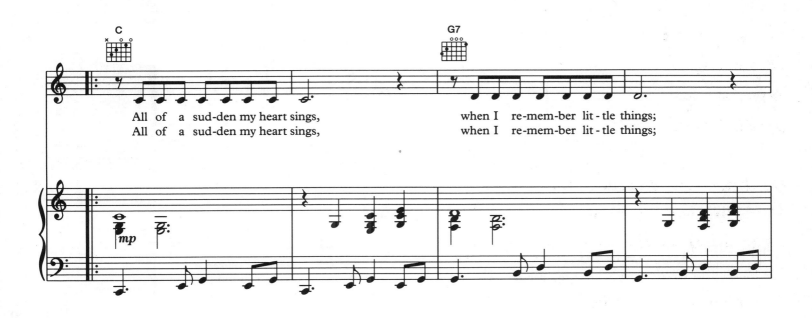

All of a sud-den my heart sings, when I re-mem-ber lit-tle things;
All of a sud-den my heart sings, when I re-mem-ber lit-tle things;

the way you dance and hold me tight, the way you kiss and say good-night,
your voice up-on the te-le-phone, the lit-tle laugh that's all your own,

ALMOST LIKE BEING IN LOVE

Words by ALAN JAY LERNER
Music by FREDERICK LOEWE

AS TIME GOES BY

Words and Music by HERMAN HUPFIELD

BE MY LOVE

Words by SAMMY CAHN
Music by NIKOLOUS BRODSZKY

BEWITCHED

Words by LORENZ HART
Music by RICHARD RODGERS

BLUEBERRY HILL

Words and Music by AL LEWIS,
LARRY STOCK and VINCENT ROSE

REFRAIN

THE ANNIVERSARY WALTZ

Words and Music by AL DUBIN and DAVE FRANKLIN

COMING HOME

Words and Music by BILLY REID

DON'T FENCE ME IN

Words and Music by COLE PORTER

DANCE BALLERINA DANCE

Words by BOB RUSSELL
Music by CARL SIGMAN

Moderately- with very marked rhythm

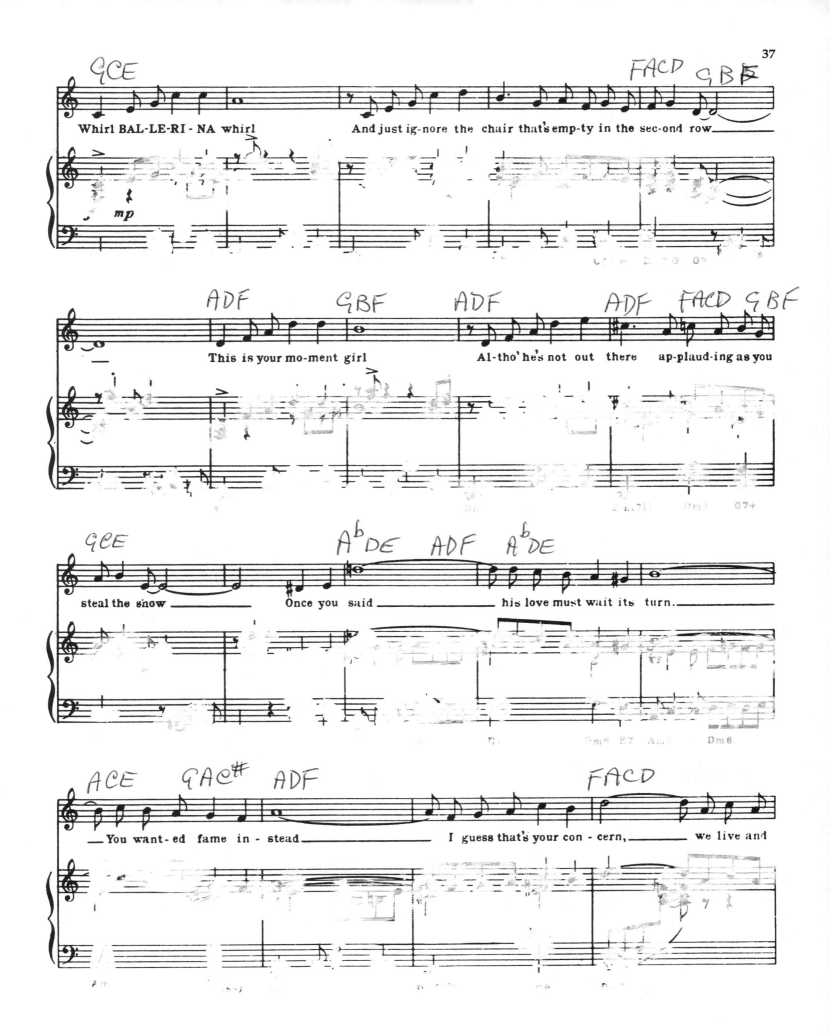

DON'T GET AROUND MUCH ANY MORE

Words by BOB RUSSELL
Music by DUKE ELLINGTON

DOWN IN THE GLEN

Words and Music by HARRY GORDON and TOMMIE CONNOR

DREAM

Words and Music by JOHNNY MERCER

Get in touch with that sun-down fel-low_____ as he tip-toes a-cross the sand.

He's got a mil-lion kinds of star-dust, pick your fav-ourite brand, and:

EV'RY TIME WE SAY GOODBYE

Words and Music by COLE PORTER

A GAL IN CALICO

Words by LEO ROBIN
Music by ARTHUR SCHWARTZ

THE HEATHER ON THE HILL

Words by ALAN JAY LERNER
Music by FREDERICK LOEWE

HOW ABOUT YOU

Words by RALPH FREED
Music by BURTON LANE

HOW ARE THINGS IN GLOCCA MORRA?

Words by E Y HARBURG
Music by BURTON LANE

HOW CAN YOU BUY KILLARNEY

Words and Music by HAMILTON KENNEDY, FREDDIE GRANT,
GERALD MORRISON and TED STEELS

HOW HIGH THE MOON

Words by NANCY HAMILTON
Music by MORGAN LEWIS

THE GIPSY

Words and Music by BILLY REID

74

I DON'T WANT TO SET THE WORLD ON FIRE

Words and Music by EDDIE SEILER, SOL MARCUS, BENNIE BENJAMIN
and EDDIE DURHAM

I DON'T WANT TO WALK WITHOUT YOU

Words by FRANK LOESSER
Music by JULE STYNE

I KNOW WHY AND SO DO YOU

81

Words by MACK GORDON
Music by HARRY WARREN

I LOVE YOU FOR SENTIMENTAL REASONS

Words by DEEK WATSON
Music by WILLIAM BEST

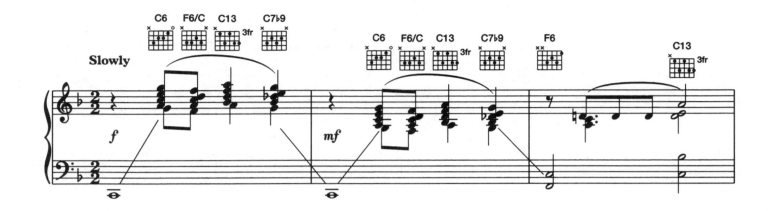

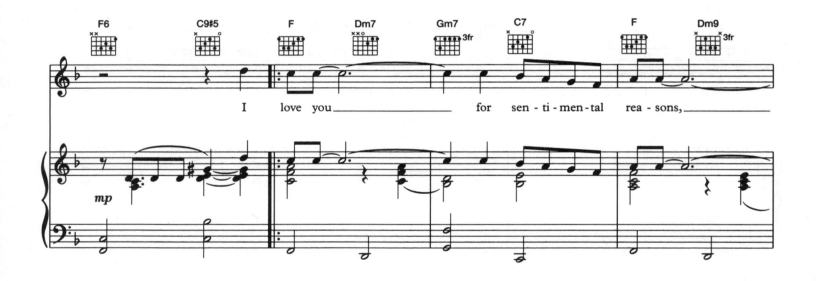

I love you _____ for sen - ti - men - tal rea - sons, _____

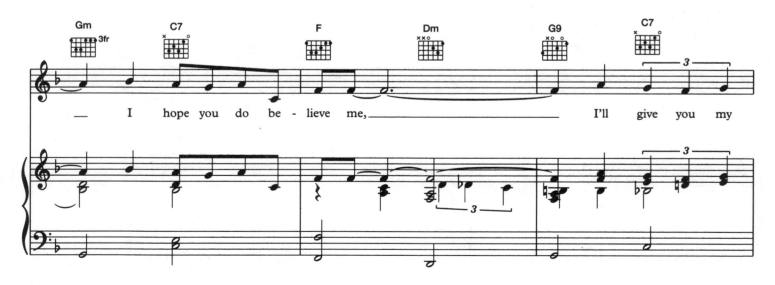

__ I hope you do be - lieve me, _____ I'll give you my

I, YI, YI, YI, YI LIKE YOU VERY MUCH

Words by MACK GORDON
Music by HARRY WARREN

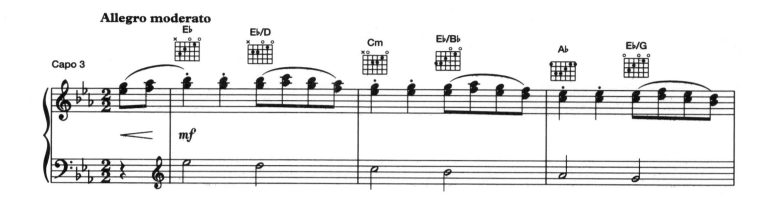

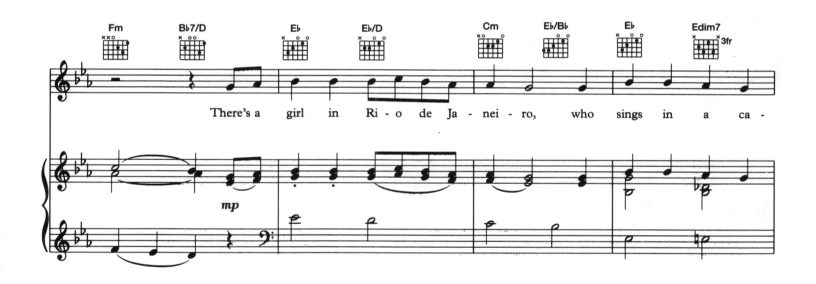

There's a girl in Ri-o de Ja-nei-ro, who sings in a ca-

-fé, _____ with a smile that's so en-tranc-ing, so sweet, so cute, so

I REMEMBER YOU

Words by JOHNNY MERCER
Music by VICTOR SCHERTZINGER

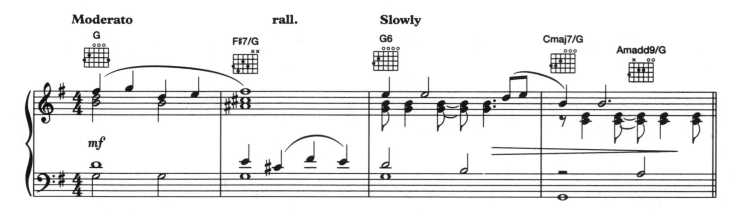

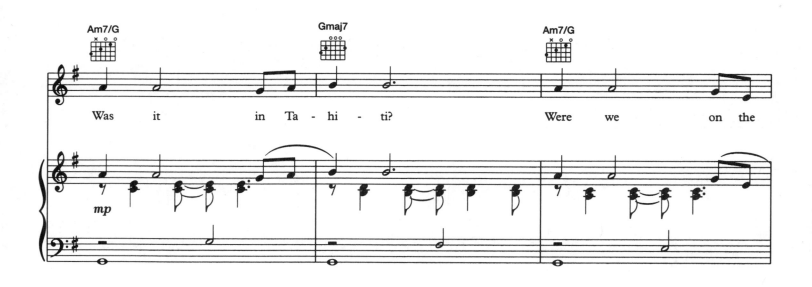

Was it in Ta - hi - ti? Were we on the

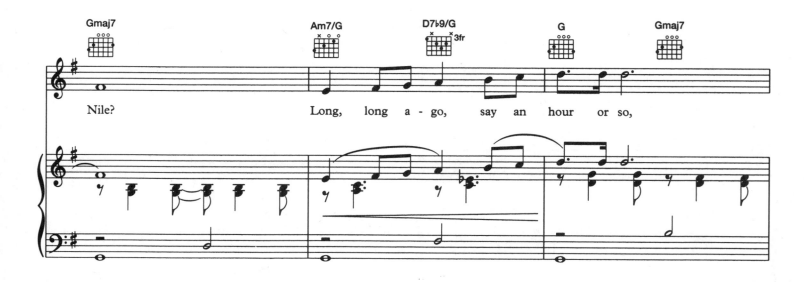

Nile? Long, long a - go, say an hour or so,

I'LL BE SEEING YOU

Words by IRVING KAHAL
Music by SAMMY FAIN

I'LL CLOSE MY EYES

Words and Music by BILLY REID

I'LL MAKE UP FOR EV'RYTHING

Words and Music by ROSS PARKER

I'VE HEARD THAT SONG BEFORE

Words and Music by JULE STYNE and SAMMY CAHN

I'LL WALK ALONE

Words by SAMMY CAHN
Music by JULE STYNE

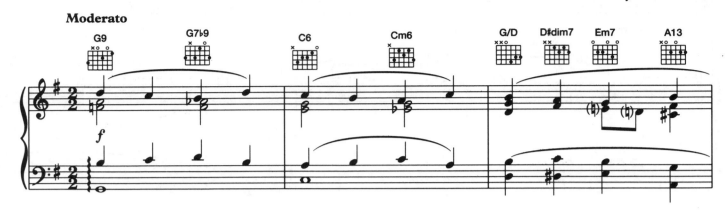

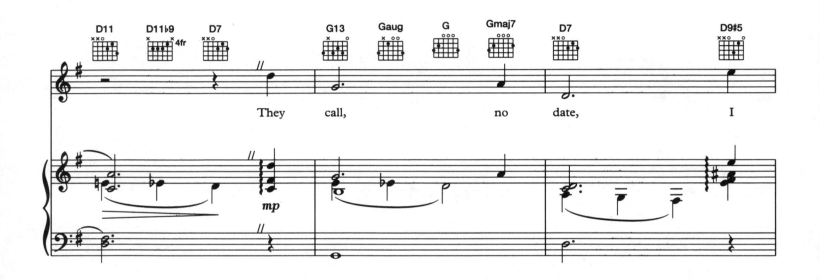

They call, no date, I

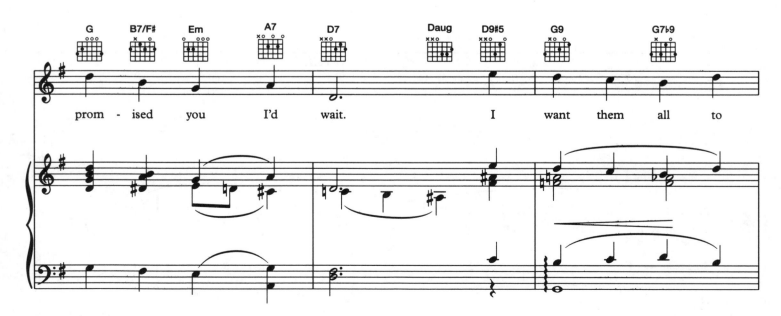

prom - ised you I'd wait. I want them all to

IT MIGHT AS WELL BE SPRING

Words by OSCAR HAMMERSTEIN II
Music by RICHARD RODGERS

IN THE MOOD

Words by JOE GARLAND

Mis - ter What-cha-call - um, what-cha do - 'in to - night?__ Hope you're in the mood, be - cause I'm
Mis - ter What-cha-call - um, all you need - ed was fun __ You can see the won - ders that this

feel - in' just right __ How's a - bout a cor - ner with a ta - ble for two __
ev' - nin' has done __ Your feet were so hea - vy till they hard - ly could move __

Where the mu - sic's mel - low in some gay ren - dez - vous?__ There's no chance ro - man - cin' with a
Now they're light as feath - ers and you're right in the groove__ You were on - ly hun - gry for some

121

LET THERE BE LOVE

Words by IAN GRANT
Music by LIONEL RAND

124

REFRAIN

THE LAST TIME I SAW PARIS

Words by OSCAR HAMMERSTEIN II
Music by JEROME KERN

Lone-ly men with lone-ly eyes are seek-ing her in vain, Her
Chil-dren who ap-plaud-ed Punch and Ju-dy in the park, And

streets are where they were, but there's no sign of her She has left the Seine.
those who danced at night, and kept their Par-is bright Till the town went dark.

REFRAIN

(simply - with rhythm preserved - not sadly)

The last time I saw Par-is Her heart was warm and

gay, I heard the laugh-ter of her heart in ev-'ry street ca-

fé.   The last time I saw Par - is,   Her   trees were dressed for

spring,   And lov - ers walked be - neath those trees, and

birds found songs to sing.   I dodged the same old tax - i - cabs that

(brightly)

I had dodged for   years;   The   cho - rus of their

LAURA

Words by JOHNNY MERCER
Music by DAVID RAKSIN

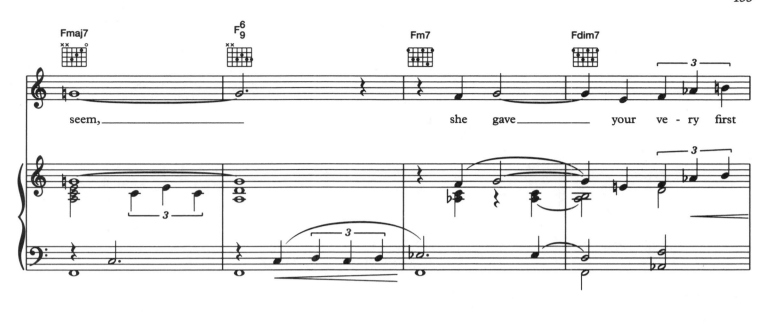

seem, _____ she gave _____ your ve - ry first

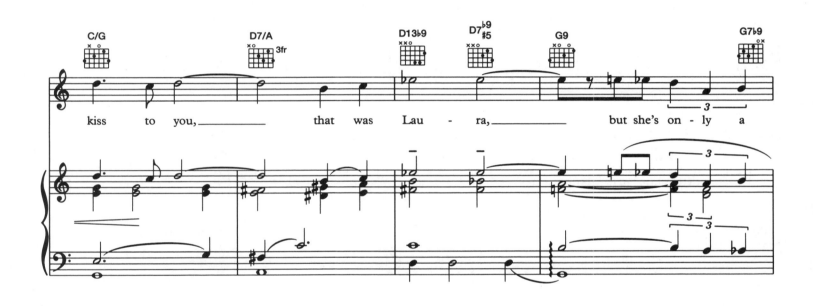

kiss to you, _____ that was Lau - ra, _____ but she's on - ly a

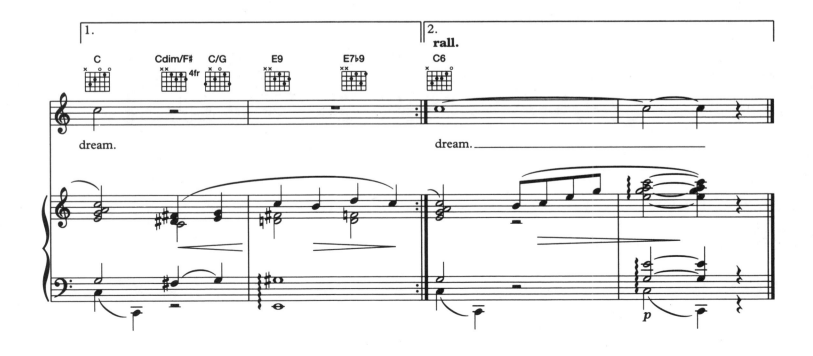

dream.   dream. _____

LILLI MARLENE

Words by TOMMIE CONNOR
Original Words by HANS LEIP
Music by NORBERT SHULTZE

Or-ders came for sail-ing some-where o-ver there, All con-fined to bar-racks was
Rest-ing in a bill-et just be-hind the line, Ev-en tho' we're part-ed your

C G7

more than I could bear; I knew you were wait-ing in the street, I heard your feet, But
lips are close to mine; You wait where that lan-tern soft-ly gleams, Your sweet face seems, To

C C7 F C G7

could not meet; My Lil-li of the lamp-light, My own LIL-LI MAR-
haunt my dreams, My Lil-li of the lamp-light, My own LIL-LI MAR-

F C Dm7 G7 C G7

1.

Last time

-LENE.

f

rit

ff

C Cdim Dm7 G7 C F C G7 Dm7 G7 C

A LOVELY WAY TO SPEND AN EVENING

Words by HAROLD ADAMSON
Music by JIMMY McHUGH

138

LONG AGO (AND FAR AWAY)

Words by IRA GERSHWIN
Music by JEROME KERN

MONA LISA

Words and Music by JAY LIVINGSTON and RAY EVANS

MAM'SELLE

Words by MACK GORDON
Music by EDMUND GOULDING

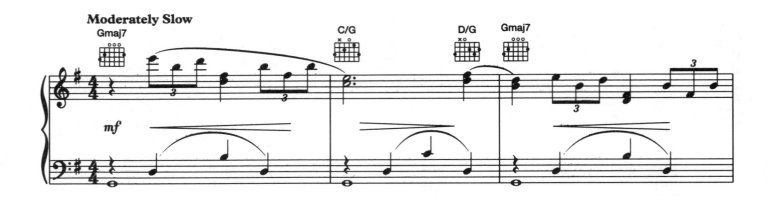

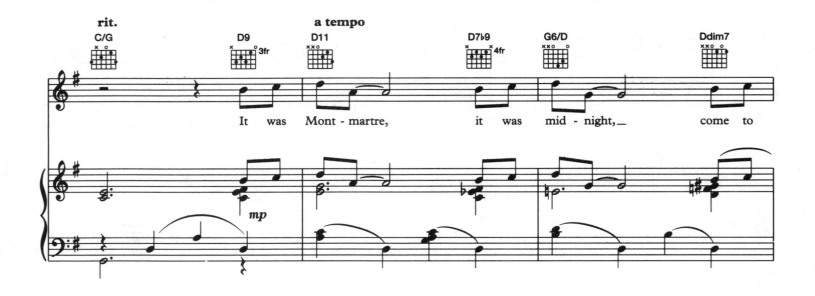

MAYBE IT'S BECAUSE I'M A LONDONER

Words and Music by
HUBERT GREGG

REFRAIN **Slowly** (*with feeling*)

May-be it's because I'm a Lon-doner——— That I love Lon-don so,

F Cm D7 G7 Db9 C7 G9 C7 F

mp mf a tempo

Maybe it's because I'm a Lon-doner—That I think of her—Wherever I go. I

Cm D7 G7 dim G7 Gm Eb7 C7

get a fun-ny feel-ing in-side of me——— Just walk-ing up and down,———

F Cm D7 G7 Db9 C7 G9 C7 A7+ A7

Maybe it's because I'm a Londoner That I love Lon-don Town. Town.

C D7 Bb Bdim F D7 G9 C7 F G7 C7 F

MOONLIGHT BECOMES YOU

Words by JOHNNY BURKE
Music by JIMMY VAN HEUSEN

**SEE P. 56 FOR
INTRODUCTION AND VERSE**

REFRAIN

Molto Moderato con expressione

INTRODUCTION AND VERSE

VERSE

Stand there just a mo - ment, dar-ling, let me catch my breath.

I've nev-er see a pic - ture quite so love - ly.

How did you ev - er learn to look so love - ly?

THE MORE I SEE YOU

Words by MACK GORDON
Music by HARRY WARREN

SEE P. 42 FOR
INTRODUCTION AND VERSE

REFRAIN

The more I see you,___ The more I want you.___ Somehow this

feel - ing___ just grows and grows.___ With ev-'ry sigh I be -

-come more mad a - bout you,___ more lost with-out you___ And so it

INTRODUCTON AND VERSE

Each time I look at you is like the first time,___ Each time you're

near me,___the thrill is new.___ And there is nothing that I would-n't

do for, the rare de-light of___ thesight of you. For;___

MY FOOLISH HEART

Words by NED WASHINGTON
Music by VICTOR YOUNG

REFRAIN Slowly and expressively

160

A NIGHTINGALE SANG IN BERKELEY SQUARE

Words by ERIC MASCHWITZ
Music by MANNING SHERWIN

*Pronounced **Bar** - klee

NEAR YOU

Words by KERMIT GOELL
Music by FRANCIS CRAIG

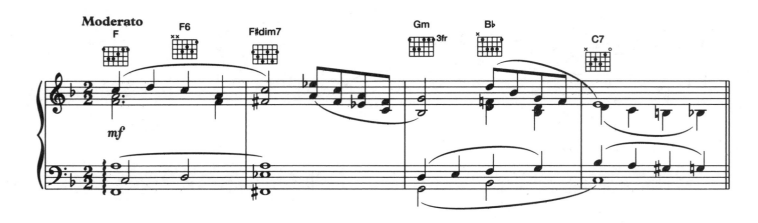

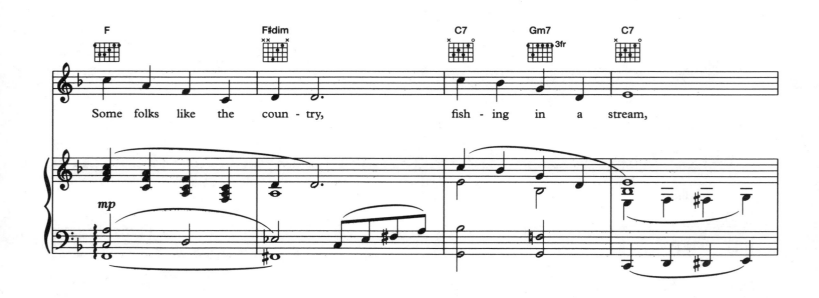

Some folks like the coun-try, fish-ing in a stream,

oth - ers like the moun - tains, that's where they can dream.

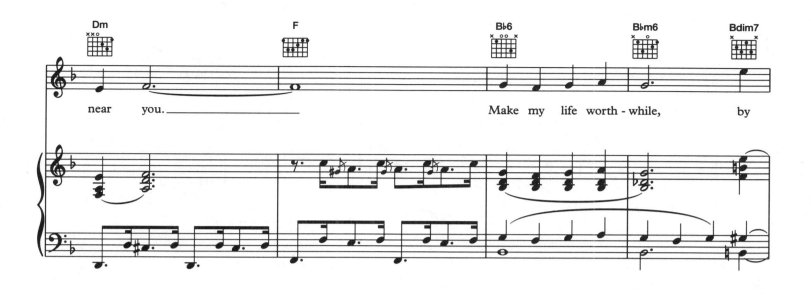

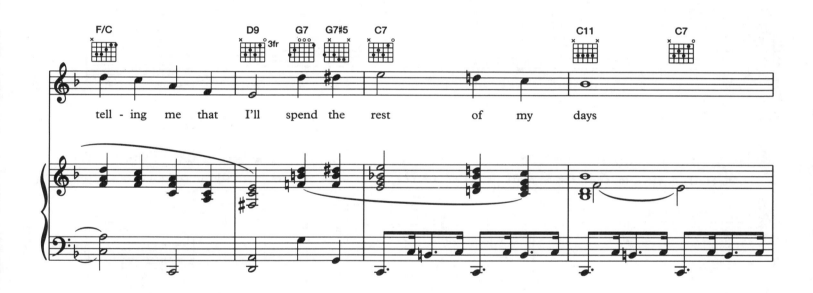

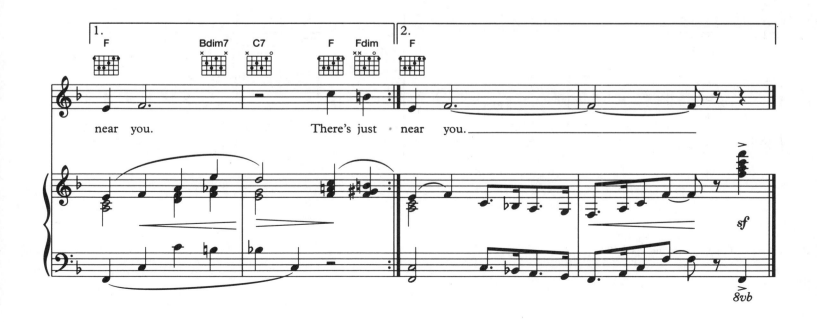

THE NEARNESS OF YOU

Words by NED WASHINGTON
Music by HOAGY CARMICHAEL

NOW IS THE HOUR

Words by MAEWA KAIHAU
Music by CLEMENT SCOTT

Andante molto espress.

1. Now is the hour ____ When we must say good ____ bye; ____
2. I'll dream of you ____ If you will dream of me; ____
3. Ha ____ e ____ re ra ____ Te ma ____ na ta ____ ngi pai; ____

OUR LOVE AFFAIR

Words and Music by ARTHUR FREED and ROGER EDENS

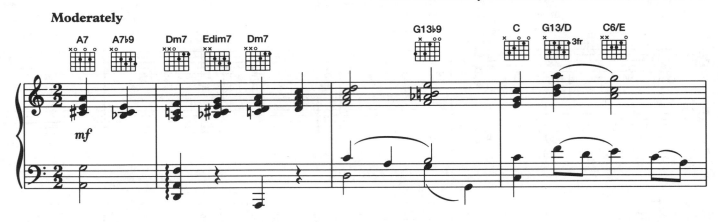

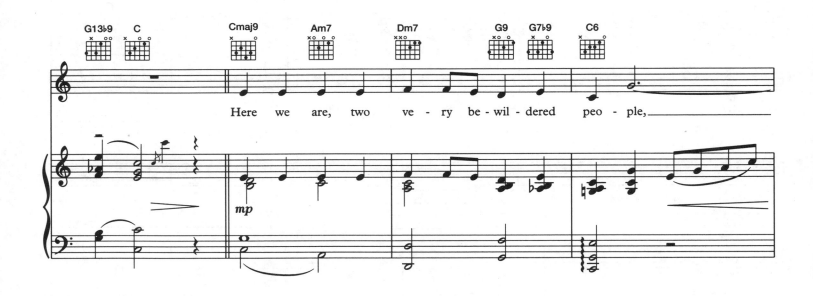

Here we are, two ve-ry be-wil-dered peo-ple,

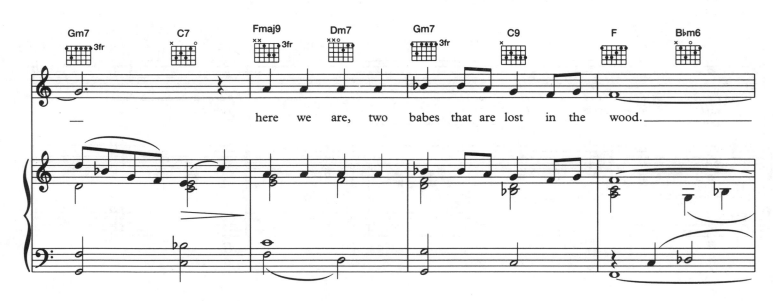

here we are, two babes that are lost in the wood.

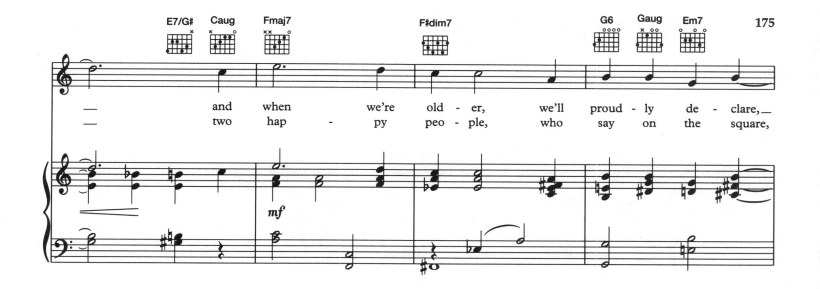

and when we're old- er, we'll proud- ly de - clare,—
two hap - py peo - ple, who say on the square,

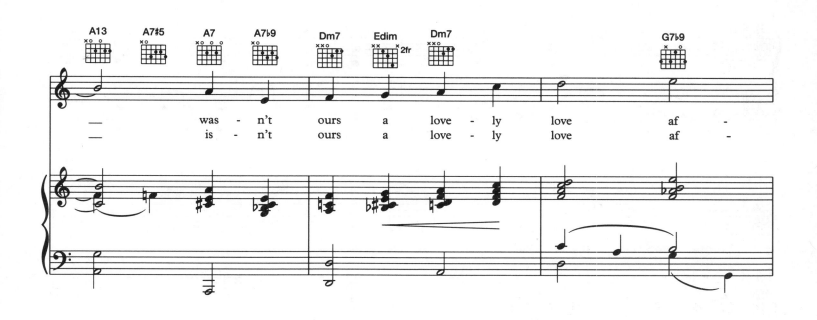

— was - n't ours a love - ly love af -
— is - n't ours a love - ly love af -

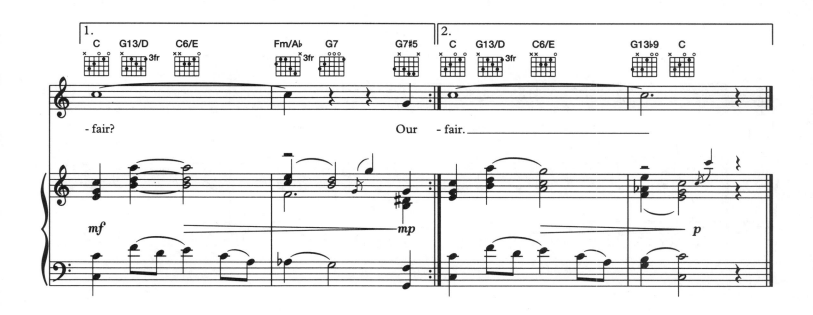

- fair? Our - fair. _____

PISTOL PACKIN' MAMA

Words and Music by AL DEXTER

Lyrics:

Lay that pis-tol down, babe, lay that pis-tol down, pis-tol pack-in' ma-ma,__ lay that pis-tol down!

Drink-in' beer in a ca-bar-et,__ and I was hav-in' fun! Un-

PAPER DOLL

Words and Music
by JOHNNY S BLACK

RED ROSES FOR A BLUE LADY

Words and Music by SID TEPPER and ROY C BENNETT

ROOM FIVE-HUNDRED-AND-FOUR

Words by ERIC MASCHWITZ
Music by GEORGE POSFORD

SAND IN MY SHOES

Words by FRANK LOESSER
Music by VICTOR SCHERTZINGER

'Out of sight, out of mind', ____ that's what I told my-self. ____

So I left you be - hind, and I con - trolled my - self. ____

Yet some my-ste-ri-ous thing___ makes ev-ery me-mo-ry cling.

It makes me want to take wing___ a-gain to-

-night, and know the de-light of hold-ing you

beguine tempo

tight.___ Sand in my shoes,___

SCARLET RIBBONS

Words by JACK SEGAL
Music by EVELYN DANZIG

THE SEA (LA MER)

Original Words and Music by CHARLES TRENET
English Words by CARLENE MAIR

THE STARS WILL REMEMBER

Words and Music by
DON PELOSI and LEO TOWERS

SENTIMENTAL JOURNEY

Words and Music by BUD GREEN, LES BROWN and BEN HOMER

Ev-ery roll-ing stone gets to feel a-lone when home sweet home is far a-way,

I'm a roll-ing stone who's been so a-lone un-til to-day.

Gon-na take a sen-ti-men-tal jour-ney, gon-na set my

TANGERINE

Words by JOHNNY MERCER
Music by VICTOR SCHERTZINGER

South A - me - ri - can stor - ies _____ tell of a girl who's quite a dream,

the beau - ty of her race. Though you doubt all the stor - ies, _____

TAKING A CHANCE ON LOVE

Words by JOHN LATOUCHE and TED FETTER
Music by VERNON DUKE

TENDERLY

Words by JACK LAWRENCE
Music by WALTER GROSS

Valse moderato

THAT LOVELY WEEKEND

Words and Music by
MOIRA and TED HEATH

THAT OLD BLACK MAGIC

Words by JOHNNY MERCER
Music by HAROLD ARLEN

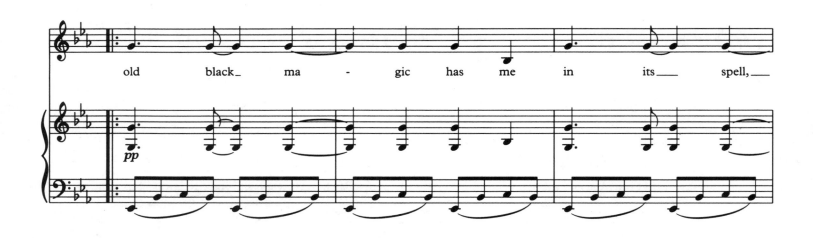

old black ma - gic has me in its spell,

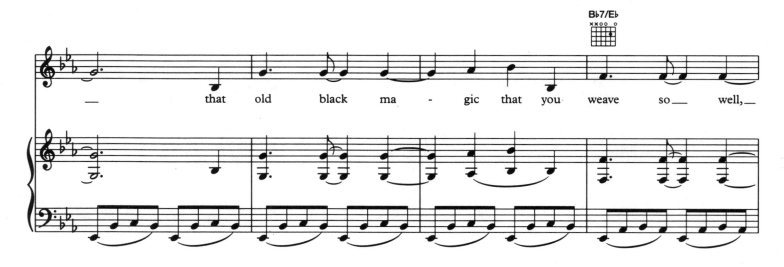

that old black ma - gic that you weave so well,

THERE GOES THAT SONG AGAIN

Words by SAMMY CAHN
Music by JULE STYNE

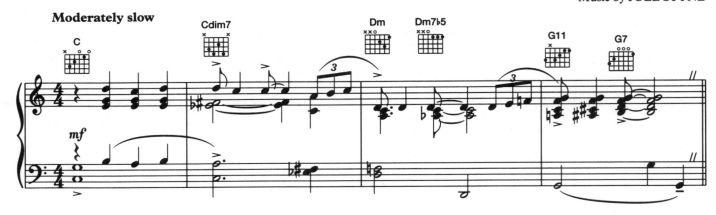

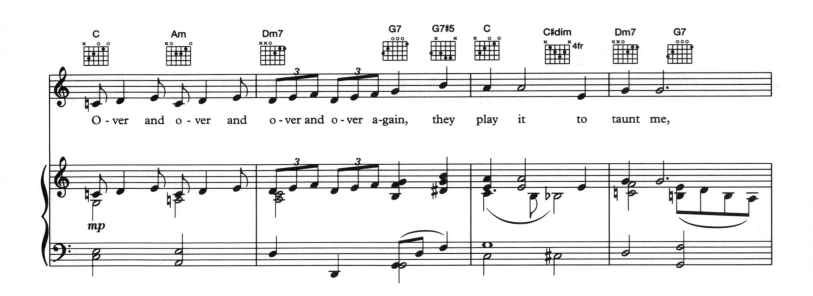

O- ver and o -ver and o -ver and o -ver a-gain, they play it to taunt me,

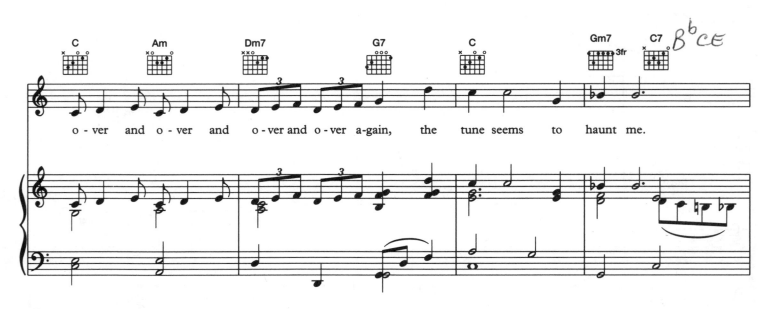

o- ver and o -ver and o -ver and o -ver a-gain, the tune seems to haunt me.

225

THAT LUCKY OLD SUN

Words by HAVEN GILLESPIE
Music by BEASLEY SMITH

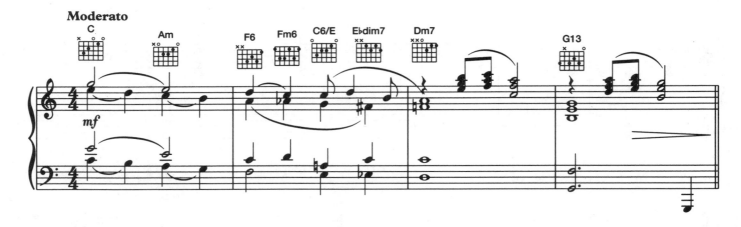

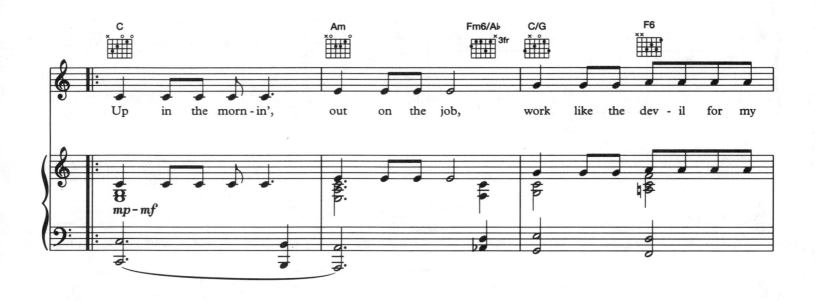

Up in the morn-in', out on the job, work like the dev-il for my

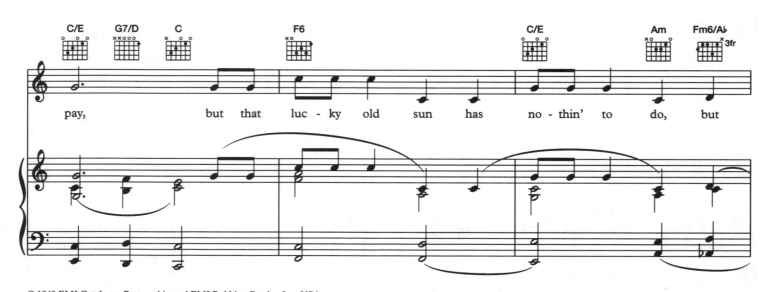

pay, but that luc-ky old sun has no-thin' to do, but

TIME AFTER TIME

Words by SAMMY CAHN
Music by JULE STYNE

SEE P.231 FOR
INTRODUCTION AND VERSE

INTRODUCTON AND VERSE

THE TROLLEY SONG

Words and Music by HUGH MARTIN and RALPH BLANE

WE'LL GATHER LILACS

Words and Music by IVOR NOVELLO

WHEN YOU WISH UPON A STAR

Words by NED WASHINGTON
Music by LEIGH HARLINE

243

WHISPERING GRASS

Words by FRED FISHER
Music by DORIS FISHER

THE WHITE CLIFFS OF DOVER

Words by NAT BURTON
Music by WALTER KENT

WE'LL KEEP A WELCOME

Words by LYN JOSHUA and JAMES HARPER
Music by MAI JONES

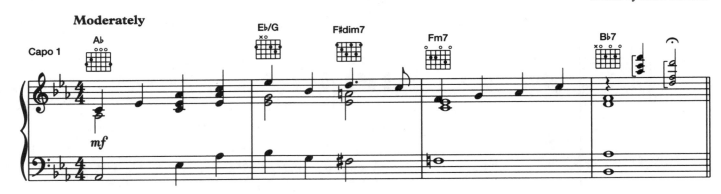

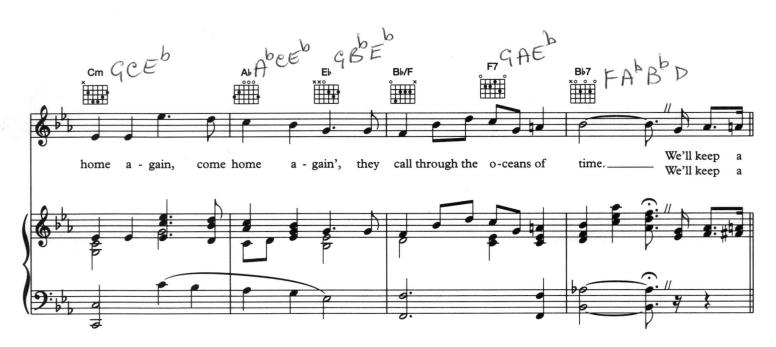

YES MY DARLING DAUGHTER

Words and Music by JACK LAWRENCE and ALBERT SIRMAY

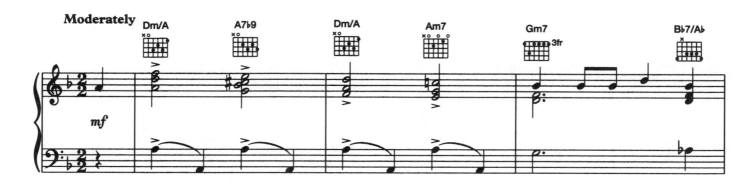

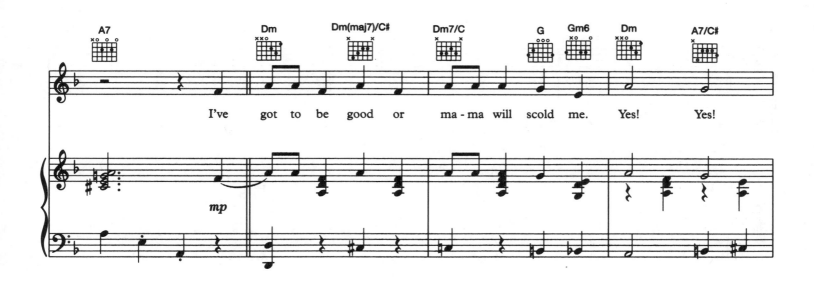

I've got to be good or ma-ma will scold me. Yes! Yes!

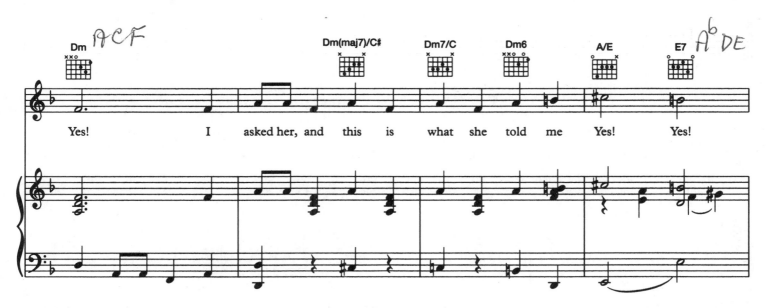

Yes! I asked her, and this is what she told me Yes! Yes!

YOU'D BE SO NICE TO COME HOME TO

Words and Music by COLE PORTER

REFRAIN (*Rather slow with feeling*)

256

YOU'VE DONE SOMETHING TO MY HEART

Words by FRANK EYTON and IAN GRANT
Music by NOEL GAY

YOU'LL NEVER KNOW

Words by MACK GORDON
Music by HARRY WARREN

YOURS

Words by JACK SHERR
Music by GONZALO ROIG

This night has mu - sic   The sweet - est
(The cloak of) eve - ning   is wrapp'd a -

mu - sic,   It ech - oes some - thing with - in my heart!
round us,   There is a spell in its mys - tic blue!

I hold you near me,   Oh dar - ling hear me,   I have a
This won-d'rous eve - ning   The moon has found us,   It hears me

264

ZIP-A-DEE-DOO-DAH

Words by RAY GILBERT
Music by ALLIE WRUBEL

SEE P.267 FOR
INTRODUCTION AND VERSE

VERSE
Moderately fast

INTRODUCTON AND VERSE

100 YEARS OF POPULAR MUSIC

9816A

Vol. 1 - 9817A

Vol. 2 - 9818A

Vol. 1 - 9819A

Vol. 2 - 9820A

Vol. 1 - 9821A

Vol. 2 - 9822A

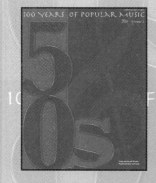

Vol. 1 - 9823A

Vol. 2 - 9824A

Vol. 1 - 9825A

Vol. 2 - 9826A

Vol. 1 - 9827A

Vol. 2 - 9828A

Vol. 1 - 9829A

Vol. 2 - 9830A

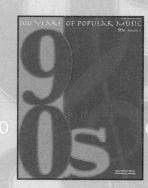

Vol. 1 - 9831A

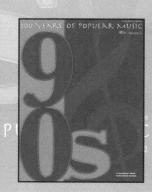

Vol. 2 - 9832A

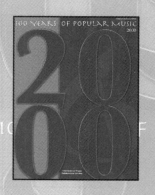

9833A

IMP
International
MUSIC
Publications

IMP's Exciting New Series!